Middle- Earth
Riddle
Book

The Middle-Earth Riddle Book

Bridegroom Press   Plano, TX

Copyright 2005 by Steve Kellmeyer

ISBN:0-9767368-4-5

Printed in the U.S.A.
Bridegroom Press
2901 Country Place Dr
Plano, TX 75075
www.bridegroompress.com
E-mail: info@bridegroompress.com
Phone : 877-348-6195

Riddles

(The Answer Key begins on Page 87)

1.

What goes on four legs in the morning,
Two legs at noon
and three legs in the evening?

Answer #47

2.

Touching one, yet holding two,
It is a one-link chain.
Binding those who keep words true,
'Till death doth rend it twain.

Answer #35

3.

Say my name
And I disappear.

Answer #27

4.

The larger I am,
The harder it is to see me.

Answer #53

5.

No wings, nor feet unto my share have fell,
Yet I in swiftness do the best excel.
Arms I have none, nor weapons do I wear,
And yet I daily wound the brave and fair.
My name is odious to friends and foes,
Yet I'm admired by all the Belles and Beaus.
And when my name's concealed, I've many friends,
The best man fears me, and his fault amends.
All wise men hate me, as their common foe,
Take C from me, I keep you from the snow.
Old maids caress me, for this world I hate,
As it hates them, so we receive our fate.
From these short hints, to tell my name's your task,
That well performed, I've nothing more to ask.

Answer #16

6.

A bridge of pearls its form uprears
High o'er a grey and misty sea;
E'en in a moment it appears,
And rises upwards giddily.

Beneath its arch can find a road
The loftiest vessel's mast most high,
Itself hath never borne a load,
And seems, when thou draw'st near, to fly.

It comes first with the stream, and goes
Soon as the wat'ry flood is dried.
Where may be found this bridge, disclose,
And who its beauteous form supplied!
                              -Friederich Schiller

Answer #29

7.

What is smaller than a mouse
And has more windows than a house?

Answer #1

8.

A ship there drives upon the tide,
That sails doth bear, she hath no mast.
But one oar she hath on each side;
Her sails the snow in whiteness pass.
In her front wears two lanterns bright;
But when she is upon point to fall,
Then lend an ear, for great delight
Of musick she affords to all.

Answer #72

9.

I am always hungry,
I must always be fed,
The finger I lick
Will soon turn red.

Answer #80

10.

Over the water,
And under the water,
And always with its head down.

Answer #25

11.

I give you a group of three #
One is sitting down,
And will never get up.
The second eats as much as is given him,
Yet is always hungry.
The third goes away and never returns.

Answer #15

12.

A priest and a friar and a wise old man
Went to a pear tree, where three pears hang.
Each one took a pear,
How many hang there?

Answer #28

13.

Only two backbones, a thousand ribs.

Answer #38

14.

A box without hinges, key, or lid,
Yet golden tresure inside is hid.
_J.R.R. Tolkien

Answer #158

15.

Who was he that was never born,
Was then buried in his mother's womb,
and after death was baptized?

Answer #50

16.

Thirty-two white cows
Standing in a stall,
Along comes a red cow
And licks them one and all.

Answer #33

17.
Two lookers
Two crookers
Four down-hangers
And a switch-about.

Answer #44

18.
My mother brought me forth,
Then, shortly afterward,
I, her daughter, brought her forth again.

Answer #32

19.
Tell me, what foeman is worst to subdue?
And what sickness lasts a lifetime through?
Of men that are upright, say which is the best?
Of those that are wicked, who passeth the rest?

Answer #22

20.

A man without eyes
Saw plums on a tree.
He neither took plums
Nor left plums
How can this be?

Answer #41

21.

I saw maidens like dust,
Rocks were their beds,
They were black and swarthy in the sunshine,
but the darker it grew,
The fairer they became.

Answer #17

22.

Houseful
Yardful
You can't catch a
Spoonful.

Answer #6

23.

At night they come without being fetched,
And by day they are lost without being stolen.

Answer #67

24.

Out of the eater came forth something to eat
Out of the strong came forth something sweet.
(Judges 4:14)

Answer #77

25.

I scream shrill across the earth
I shatter the oak's tremendous girth
Beat upon the very skies
And sweep the fields with endless sighs.

Answer #5

26.

Round as a biscuit
And deep as a cup
All the king's horses
Couldn't pull it up.

Answer #78

27.

I am sitting above a horse which was not born,
Whose mother I hold in my hand.

Answer #63

28.

What weeps tears without an eye
Makes everything visible
But does not see its own garment?

Answer #10

29.

What stands on one leg
With its heart in its head?

Answer #81

30.

What is he that builds stronger than either
The mason, the shipwright or the carpenter?
-Shakespeare

Answer #100

31.

A bird it is, whose rapid motion
With eagle's flight divides the air;
A fish it is, and parts the ocean,
That bore a greater monster ne'er;
An elephant it is, whose rider
On his broad back a tower has put:
'Tis like the reptile base, the spider,
Whenever it extends its foot,
And when, with iron tooth projecting,
It seeks its own life-blood to drain,
On footing firm, itself erecting,
It braves the raging hurricane.
- Friederich Schiller,

Answer #49

32.

In marble walls as white as milk,
Lined with skin of softest silk,
Within a fountain crystal clear,
A golden apple doth appear.
No doors there are to this stronghold,
Yet thieves break in and steal the gold.

Answer #37

33.

I am just two and two, I am warm, I am cold,
And the parent of numbers that cannot be told.
I am lawful, unlawful - a duty, a fault,
I am often sold dear, good for nothing when bought;
An extraordinary boon, and a matter of course,
And yielded with pleasure when taken by force.
                                - William Cowper

Answer #76

34.

'Twas whispered in heaven, 'twas muttered in hell,
And echo caught faintly the sound as it fell;
On the confines of earth 'twas permitted to rest,
And the depth of the ocean its presence confessed...
Yet in shade let it rest, like a delicate flower,
Ah, breathe on it softly, it dies in an hour.
-Lord Byron

Answer #11

35.

As light as a feather, but
You can't hold it for ten minutes.

Answer #95

36.

Hickamore Hackamore
On the king's kitchen door.
All the king's horses
And all the king's men
Couldn't pull Hickamore Hackamore
Off the king's kitchen door.

Answer #21

37.

In walking 'cross a field,
I found something good to eat.
It was not flesh and it was not bone.
I kept it 'til it ran alone.

Answer #45

38.

Has four legs and a foot
But can't walk
Has four legs and a head
But can't talk.

Answer #57

39.

All-ruling Tyrant of the Earth,
To vilest Slaves I owe my birth.
How is the greatest Monarch blest,
When in my gaudy Liv'ry dressed!
No haughty Nymphy has Powe'r to run
From me; or my Embraces shun.
Stabbed to the Heart, condemned to Flame,
My constancy is still the same.

Answer #99

40.

Each morning I appear
To lie at your feet,
All day I will follow
No matter how fast you run,
Yet I nearly perish
In the midday sun.

Answer #69

41.

If man carried my burden
He would break his back.
I am not rich,
But leave silver in my track.

Answer #54

42.

Runs over fields and woods all day
Under the bed at night sits not alone,
With long tongue hanging out,
A-waiting for a bone.

Answer #34

43.

Pronounced as one letter,
And written with three,
Two letters there are,
And two only in me.
I'm double, I'm single,
I'm black blue and grey,
I'm read from both ends,
And the same either way.

Answer #88

44.

There was a prophet on this earth,
His age no man could tell;
He was at his greatest height
Before e'er Adam fell.
His wives are very numerous,
Yet he takes care of none;
And at the day of reckoning
He bids them all begon.
He wears his boots when he should sleep;
His spurs are ever new;
There's not a shoemaker on the earth
Can fit him for a shoe.

Answer #66

45.

I live within a dwelling of stone,
There buried in slumber I dally;
Yet, armed with a weapon of iron alone,
The foe to encounter I sally.
At first I'm invisible, feeble, and mean,
And o'er me thy breath has dominion;
I'm easily drowned in a raindrop e'en,
Yet in victory waxes my pinion.
When my sister, all-powerful, gives me her hand,
To the terrible lord of the world I expand.

Answer #3

46.

Black I am and much admired,
Men seek me 'til they are tired;
When they find me, break my head,
And take me from my resting bed.

Answer #87

47.

Old Mother Twitchett had but one eye,
And a long tail which she let fly;
And every time she went through a gap,
A bit of her tail she left in a trap.

Answer #62

48.

Little Nanny Etticoat
In a white petticoat,
And a red nose;
The longer she stands,
The shorter she grows.

Answer #2

49.

My step is slow, the snow's my breath,
I give the ground a grinding death.
My marching makes an end of me,
Slain by sun, or drowned in sea.

Answer #24

50.

Daffy-down dilly has come to town
In a yellow petticoat and a green gown.

Answer #39

51.

Here sites the Lord Mayo,
Here sit his two men
Here sits the rooster,
Here sits the hen
Here sit the little chickens,
Here they run in.
Chin-chopper, chin-chopper, chin-chopper, chin

Answer #68

52.

As soft as silk, as white as milk,
As bitter as gall, a strong wall,
And a green coat covers me all.

Answer #93

53.

A riddle, a riddle as I suppose,
A hundred eyes, and never a nose.

Answer #115

54.

I am only useful
When I am full,
Yet I am always
Full of holes.

Answer #4

55.

Goes to the door but doesn't knock,
Goes to the window but doesn't rap,
Goes to the fire and doesn't warm,
Goes upstairs and does no harm.

Answer #23

56.

It has a tongue but never talks,
It has no legs but always walks.

Answer #34

57.

Black within and red without,
Four corners 'round about.

Answer #51

58.

As I went over London Bridge,
I saw something on the hedge.
It had four fingers and one thumb
But wasn't fish, flesh, fowl or bone.

Answer #71

59.

A long neck and no hands,
Hundred legs and can't stand,
Runs through the house in the morning,
Hides away when company comes calling.

Answer #91

60.

As round as an apple,
As deep as a pail;
It never cries out
Till it's caught by the tail.

Answer #111

61.

Higher than a house,
Higher than a tree
Oh whatever
Can this be?

Answer #121

62.

Behind the bush, behind the thorn,
I heard a stout man blow his horn,
He was booted and spurred, and stood with pride,
With golden feathers at his side;
His beard was flesh, his mouth was horn,
I am sure such a man never could have been born.

Answer #141

63.

Formed long ago, yet made today,
Employed while others sleep;
What few would like to give away,
Nor any wish to keep.

Answer #8

64.

A hill full, a hole full,
You cannot catch a bowl full.

Answer #30

65.

Lives in winter
Dies in summer
And grows with its roots upward!

Answer #60

66.

Wings on the water
Wonder in motion,
A beak of brass
Apt for brawling.
But fear and foulness
Fill my belly,
Pity all
Who ache inside me;
Whip-stung, woeful
Weak and weary.

Answer #89

67.

What we caught we threw away;
What we didn't catch, we kept.

Answer #12

68.

He went to the wood and caught it;
He sat him down and sought it,
Because he could not find it
Home with him he brought it.

Answer #143

69.

I can be touched
But I hurt those who touch me
I move swiftly through a dry forest
But die in a mountain stream
Where I pass I leave a black shroud.

Answer #119

70.

As I went through the garden gap
Who should I meet but Dick Redcap
A stick in his hand, a stone in his throat,
If you'll tell me this riddle, I'll give you a groat.

Answer #26

71.

I drive men mad
For love of me,
Easily beaten,
Never free.

Answer #152

72.

I am the part of the bird
That is not in the sky,
Who can drown in the ocean
and yet remain dry.

Answer #20

73.

Goes over all the hills and hollows,
Bites hard, but never swallows.

Answer #40

74.

Has a mouth but does not speak,
Has a bed but never sleeps.

Answer #61

75.

This darksome burn, horseback brown,
His rollock highroad roaring down,
In coop and in comb
The fleece of his foam
Flutes and low to the body falls home.
                    - Gerard Manley Hopkins

Answer #75

79.

It goes up and down a tree
It has eyes but cannot see.

Answer #19

80.

I'm alive at both ends
And dead in the middle
If you guess this riddle
I'll give you a fiddle.

Answer #151

81.

Eeno and
Ino,
Fido and
Dido,
Which one was the big dog?

Answer #123

76.

I turn around once,
What is out will not get in.
I turn around again,
What is in will not get out.

Answer #86

77.

All about, but cannot be seen,
Can be captured, cannot be held,
No throat, but can be heard.

Answer #97

78.

What goes through the door
Without pinching itself?
What sits on the stove
Without burning itself?
What sits on the table
And is not ashamed?

Answer #7

82.

Black we are and much admired;
Men seek for us till they are tired.
We tire horses, comfort man,
Guess this riddle if you can.

Answer #101

83.

I gave my love a cherry that hath no stone,
I gave my love a chicken that hath no bone,
I gave my love a thimble that hath no end,
I gave my love a baby that's a no cryin'.

Answer #79

84.

Round as a biscuit,
Busy as a bee:
Two strong hands do the work
Though fingers none can see.

Answer #13

85

Read my riddle, I pray
What God never sees,
What the king seldom sees,
What we see every day.

Answer #113

86.

I know a word of letters three.
Add two, and fewer there will be.

Answer #126

87.

Lovely and round,
I shine with pale light,
Grown in the darkness,
A lady's delight.

Answer #142

88.

All over the hills by day
Back home at night,
I sit under the bed
And gape for bones.

Answer #34

89.

The man who built it, doesn't want it.
The man who bought it, doesn't need it.
The man who needs it, doesn't know it.

Answer #136

90.

The beginning of eternity
The end of time and space
The beginning of every end,
And the end of every place.

Answer #65

91.

I sit on the ground
Finger up-raised to heaven.
I speak with clear tones
And aim for others
To go where I point.

Answer #36

92.

I wrinkled am and passing old,
But gallant is my motion,
Abhorring all to be controulled
By anyone's devotion.
Come all that list on me to mount,
Sure I will not forsake them,
But let them make their just account,
That finely I shall shake them.
Nor do I ask men ought for hose,
For shoes, for drink, or meating.
Come all that wish with me to close
Sans paying or entreating.
And they may chance find in my womb
To make them wish they were at home.

Answer #168

96.

Lighter than what I am made of,
More of me is hidden
Than is seen.

Answer #104

97.

My first displays the wealth and pomp of kings,
Lords of the earth! their luxury and ease.
Another view of man, my second brings,
Behold him there, the monarch of the seas!
But ah! united what reverse we have!
Man's boasted power and freedom, all are flown:
Lord of the earth and sea, he bends a slave,
And woman, lovely woman, reigns alone.
Thy ready wit the word will soon supply,
May its approval beam in that soft eye!
                                        -Jane Austen

Answer #124

93.

Inscribe an M above a line,
then write an E below.
The flower you seek is hung so fine,
it sways when breezes blow.

Answer #42

94.

Screaming, soaring, seeking sky,
Flowers of fire flying high.
Eastern art from ancient time,
Name me now and solve this rhyme.

Answer #128

95.

My life can be measured in hours,
I serve by being devoured.
Thin, I am quick
Fat, I am slow
Wind is my foe.

Answer #149

98.

If you break me I do not stop working,
If you touch me I may be snared,
If you lose me
Nothing will matter.

Answer #139

99.

We are little airy creatures,
All of diff'rent voice and features,
One of us in glass is set,
One of us you'll find in jet,
T'other you may see in tin,
And the fourth a box within,
If the fifth you shou'd pursue,
It can never fly from you.
                    - Jonathan Swift

Answer #85

100.

Begotten, and born, and dying with noise,
The terror of women, and pleasure of boys,
Like the fiction of poets concerning the wind,
I'm chiefly unruly, when strongest confin'd.
For silver and gold I don't trouble my head,
But all I delight in is pieces of lead;
Except when I trade with a ship or a town,
Why then I make pieces of iron go down.
One property more I would have you remark,
No lady was ever more fond of a spark;
The moment I get one my soul's all a-fire,
And I roar out my joy, and in transport expire.
- Jonathan Swift

Answer #108

101.

Glittering points
That downward thrust,
Sparkling spears
That never rust.

Answer #131

102.

Two words, my answer is only two words.
To keep me, you must give me.

Answer #73

103.

Oak and hazel are my aunts,
though I am not their kin.
My cousin grows in pod on vine;
I often have a twin.
My shape is like the sands of time
contained within a glass.
I have no legs, instead a shell;
I dwell beneath the grass.

Answer #150

104.

Never speaking, still awake,
Pleasing most when most I speak,
The delight of old and young,
Tho' I speak without a tongue.
Nought but one thing can confound me,
Many voices joining round me;
Then I fret, and rave and gabble,
Like the labourers of Babel.
Now I am a dog, or cow,
I can bark, or I can low,
I can bleat, or I can sing,
Like the warblers of the spring.
Let the love-sick bard complain,
And I mourn the cruel pain;
Let the happy swain rejoice,
And I join my helping voice;
Both are welcome, grief or joy,
I with either sport and toy.
Tho' a lady, I am stout,
Drums and trumpets bring me out;
Then I clash and roar, and rattle,
Join in all the din of battle.
Jove, with all his loudest thunder,
When I'm vext, can't keep me under;
Yet so tender is my ear,
That the lowest voice I fear;
Much I dread the courtier's fate,
When his merit's out of date,
For I hate a silent breath,
And a whisper is my death.
                           - Jonathan Swift

Answer #135

105.

I march before armies,
a thousand salute me;
My fall can bring victory,
but no one would shoot me;
The wind is my lover,
one-legged am I;
Name me and see me
at home in the sky.

Answer #107

106.

It bears thee many a mile away,
And yet its place it changes ne'er;
It has no pinions to display,
And yet conducts thee through the air.
It is the bark of swiftest motion
That every weary wanderer bore;
With speed of thought the greatest ocean
It carries thee in safety o'er;
One moment wafts thee to the shore.
                        -Johann von Schiller

Answer #70

107.

I build up castles.
I tear down mountains.
I make some men blind,
I help others to see.
What am I?

Answer #43

108.

A noun there is of plural number,
Foe to peace and tranquil slumber;
Now any other noun you take,
By adding s you plural make,
But if you add an s to this
Strange is the metamorphosis:
Plural is plural now no more,
And sweet what bitter was before.

Answer #103

109.

In youth exalted high in air,
Or bathing in the waters fair;
Nature to form me took delight,
And clad my body all in white:
My person tall, and slender waste,
On either side with fringes grac'd;
Till me that tyrant man espy'd,
And drag'd me from my mother's side:
No wonder now I look so thin;
The tyrant strip't me to the skin:
My skin he flay'd, my hair he cropt;
At head and foot my body lopt:
And then, with heart more hard than stone,
He pick't my marrow from the bone.
To vex me more, he took a freak,
To slit my tongue, and made me speak:
But, that which wonderful appears,
I speak to eyes and not to ears.
He oft employs me in disguise,
And makes me tell a thousand lyes:
To me he chiefly gives in trust
To please his malice, or his lust.
From me no secret he can hide;
I see his vanity and pride:
And my delight is to expose
His follies to his greatest foes.
All languages I can command,
Yet not a word I understand.
Without my aid, the best divine
In learning would not know a line:
The lawyer must forget his pleading,
The scholar could not shew his reading.

Nay; man, my master, is my slave:
I give command to kill or save.
Can grant ten thousand pounds a year,
And make a beggar's brat a peer.
But, while I thus my life relate,
I only hasten on my gate.
My tongue is black, my mouth is furr'd,
I hardly now can force a word.
I dye unpity'd and forgot;
And on some dunghill left to rot.
-Jonathan Swift

Answer #64

110.

What does man love more than life
Fear more than death or mortal strife
What the poor have, the rich require,
and what contented men desire,
What the miser spends and the spendthrift saves
And all men carry to their graves?

Answer #90

111.

Three lives have I.
Gentle enough to soothe the skin,
Light enough to caress the sky,
Hard enough to crack rocks.

Answer #153

112.

Who makes it, has no need of it.
Who buys it, has no use for it.
Who uses it can neither see nor feel it.

Answer #136

113.

With thieves I consort,
With the vilest, in short,
I'm quite at ease in depravity;
Yet all divines use me,
And savants can't lose me,
For I am the center of gravity.

Answer #46

114.

I at fires attend,
I am a kitchen friend;
When my nose I blow,
How the embers glow!
When the wind compels,
How my bell swells!

Answer #169

115.

What stinks while living,
But in death, smells good?

Answer #106

116.

Whoever makes it, tells it not.
Whoever takes it, knows it not.
And whoever knows it wants it not.

Answer #48

119.

Sir, I bear a rhyme excelling
In mystic force and magic spelling
Celestial sprites elucidate
All my own striving can't relate

Answer #105

120.

When young, I am sweet in the sun.
When middle-aged, I make you play.
When old, I am valued more than ever.

Answer #137

121.

Weight in my belly,
Trees on my back,
Nails in my ribs,
Feet I do lack.

Answer #49

117.

Under alien bosom I quickened with breath.
None but her children tasted of death
As we sat together in the brown wreath,
Or they fell below to the stone.

She fed me until I grew sturdy for flight,
Kept me safe in the dark of the night,
And with each of her children I would fight;
My thanks for the loan of her home.

Answer #134

118.

You heard me before,
Yet you hear me again,
Then I die,
'Till you call me again.

Answer #84

122.

Shoulders pointed high above my back,
I sings through my sides
Though I am not cracked,
My neck is curved
And my song delights
Who might I be,
Will you hear me tonight?

Answer #92

123.

Many-maned scud-thumper,
Maker of worn wood,
Shrub-ruster,
Sky-mocker,
Rave!
Portly pusher,
Wind-slave.
    - John Updike

Answer #148

124.

To unravel me
You need a simple key,
No key that was made
By locksmith's hand,
But a key that only I
Will understand.

Answer #132

125.

I am seen in the water
If seen in the sky,
I am in the rainbow,
A jay's feather,
And lapis lazuli.

Answer #52

126.

Sometimes people think me odd
More evil than the devil
And greater than God
Poor men have me
Rich men need me
If you take me
Then you'll owe me.

Answer #83

127.

You can see nothing else
When you look in my face,
I will look you in the eye
And I will never lie.

Answer #109

128.

When I am filled I can point the way,
When I am empty
Nothing moves me,
I have two skins
One without and one within.

Answer #138

129.

As a whole, I am both safe and secure.
Behead me, and I become a place of meeting.
Behead me again, and I am the partner of ready.
Restore me, and I become the domain of beasts.
What am I?

Answer #55

130.

Until I am measured I am not known,
Yet how you miss me
When I have flown.

Answer #146

131.

Tell me what a dozen rubber trees
With thirty boughs on each might be?

Answer #56

132.

I never was, am always to be,
None ever saw me, nor ever will,
And yet I am the confidence of all
Who live and breathe and on me call.

Answer #82

133.

I go around in circles
But always straight ahead,
Never complain
No matter where I am led.

Answer #140

134.

Often I battle with wind and wave,
From under the sea my charge I save,
I can master them both if my grip holds out
If not, wrenched loose, they put me to rout,
I feel out the bottom, a foreign land,
With rocks I may win, but not with sand,
If the rocks bring succor and lend support,
I'll hold against the worst of their sort.

Answer #110

135.

The worm swallows,
In darkness steals,
The song of man,
His glorious ideals,
The thieving guest,
Seeks self to sate,
But no whit the wiser
For the words it ate.

Answer #58

136.

Five hundred to start, five hundred to end,
Five in the middle is seen;
First of all figures, the first of all letters,
Take up their stations between.
Join all together, and then you will bring
Before you the name of an eminent king.

Answer #94

137.

My father and mother, for love left me
Though I was not breathing nor could I see
A kinswoman kind cared for me;
Wrapped me in her clothes as one of her own.

Answer #112

138.

The faster you work, the longer to finish,
The slower you work, the less time you're famished?

Answer #145

139.

My house is not quiet, I am not loud;
But God made us one for the other,
I am the swifter, at times the stronger,
My house more enduring, within it I hover.
At times I rest; my dwelling still runs;
Within it I lodge as long as I live.
Should we two be parted, my death is certain,
So now our two names you must give.

Answer #59

140.

I am the black child of a white father;
A wingless bird,
Flying even to the clouds of heaven.
I give birth to tears of mourning
In pupils that meet me,
And at once on my birth
I am dissolved into air.

Answer #133

141.

Headless and hard, I lie on the board
Awaiting the kiss of a warrior,
Though hooded with silver and gold, it affords
No help in the work I am called to.

When I speak, men come armed
Though a maiden's breath fills me,
With sword and and with shield
And good horses in company.

I call men to wine
And send foes to flight,
I swallow the breath of the soldier
In battle, and give the weak might.

Now ask what I'm called.

Answer #117

142.

Whilst I was engaged in sitting
I spied the dead carrying the living.

Answer #49

143.

Left in peace I never move;
But should a foe desire to prove
His mettle on me, straight I fly
Right over wall and roof-tree high.
If driven by a stroke of might,
I take, though wingless, upward flight;
No feet have I, yet 'tis my way
To jump and dance bothnight and day;
No rest I feel what time my foe
May will that I a-flying go.
No end and no beginning mine,
So strange my nature and design,
And they wo see me on the wing
May deem me well a living thing.
                              -Straparola

Answer #162

144.

I saw a woman,
She sat alone
Brooding, always brooding.

Answer #147

145.

Christ, the true giver of victories,
Created me for combat.
When my lord urged me to fight,
I often scorch mortals;
I approach the earth and,
Without a touch,
Afflict a huge host of people.
At times I gladden the minds of men,
Keeping my distance I console those
Whom I fought before;
They feel my kindness
As they once felt my fire when,
After such suffering,
I soothe their lives.

Answer #120

146.

I throw her in the air, she falls down.
I throw her down, she rises in the air.

Answer #157

147.

There is a gate, we know full well,
That stands 'twixt Heaven and Earth and Hell,
Where many for a passage venture,
But very few are found to enter;
Although 'tis open Night and Day,
They for that reason shun this way:
Both Dukes and Lords abhor its Wood,
They can't come near it for their Blood.
What other Way they take to go,
Another Time I'll let you know.
Yet Commoners with greatest Ease,
Can find an Entrance when they please.
The poorest hither march in State,
(Or they can never pass the Gate)
Like Roman Generals triumphant,
And then they take a Turn and jump on't.
If gravest Parsons here advance,
They cannot pass before they dance;
There's not a Soul that does resort here,
But strips himself to pay the Porter.
                    - Jonathan Swift

Answer #164

148.

This creature came to the meeting-place.
He had but two ears,
Though twelve hundred heads,
He had but one eye
Though two shoulders and hands,
He had but one neck
Though two feet and two arms
He had but one back
And his belly was warm.
Now tell me his name.

Answer #159

149.

A white dove flew down by the castle.
Along came a king and
Picked it up handless,
Ate it up toothless, and
Carried it away wingless.

Answer #170

150.

I am valued by men, fetched from afar,
Gleaned on hill-slopes, gathered in groves,
In dale and on down.
All day through the air,
Wings bore me aloft,
And brought me with cunning
Safe under roof.
Men steeped me in vats.
Now I have power to pummel and bind,
To cast to the earth, old man and young.
As he shall find who reaches to seize me,
Pits force against force,
That he's flat on the ground,
Stripped of his strength if he cease not his folly,
Loud in his speech, but his power despoiled
To manage his mind, his hands or his feet.
Now ask me my name, who can bind men on earth,
And lay fools low in the light of day.

Answer #102

151.

The hand sows,
The eyes harvest.

Answer #129

152.

There was a green house.
Inside the green house there was a white house
Inside the white house there was a red house.
Inside the red house there were lots of babies.

Answer #144

153.

I am within as white as snow,
Without as green as herbs that grow;
I am higher then a house,
And yet am lesser than a mouse.

Answer #118

154.

In a garden was laid
A most beautiful maid
As ever was seen in the morn;
She was made a wife
The first day of her life,
And died before she was born

Answer #155

155.

My sides are firmly laced about
Yet nothing is within;
You'll think my head is strange indeed,
It's nothing else but skin.

Answer #127

156.

In the middle of the night,
Rises one with beard bedight.
Though no astrologer he be,
He marks the hours which pass and fall;
He wears a crown, although no king;
No priest, yet he the hour doth sing;
Though spurred at heel, he is no knight;
No wife he calls his own by right,
Yet children many round him dwell.
Sharp wits youneed this thing to tell.
                              -Straparola

Answer #161

157.

By something form'd, I nothing am,
Yet ev'ry Thing that you can name;
In no Place have I ever been,
Yet everywhere I may be seen;
In all Things false, yet always true,
I'm still the same- but ever new.
Lifeless, Life's perfect Form I wear
Can show a Nose, Eye, Tongue, or Ear;
Yet neither Smell, See, Taste or Hear.
All Shapes and Features I can boast,
No Flesh, No Bones, No Blood - no Ghost:
All Colours, without Paint, put on,

And change like the Chameleon.
Swiftly I come, and enter there,
Where not a Chink lets in the Air:
Like Thought I'm in a Moment gone,
Nor can I ever be alone.
All Things on Earth I imitate,
Faster than Nature can create;
Sometimes imperial Robes I wear,
Anon in Beggar's Rags appear;
A Giant now, and straight an Elf,
I'm everyone, but ne'er my self;
Ne'er sad I mourn, ne'er glad rejoice,
I move my Lips, but want a Voice;
I ne'er was born, nor e'er can die,
Then prythee tell me what am I.
                    ~Jonathan Swift

Answer #130

158.

Amongst all serpents there is one,
Born of no earthly breed;
In fury wild it stands alone,
And in its matchless speed.

With fearful voice and headlong force
It rushes on its prey,
And sweeps the rider and his horse
In one fell swoop away.

The highest point it loves to gain;
And neither bar nor lock
Its fiery onslaught can restrain;
And arms invite its shock.

It tears in twain like tender grass,
The strongest forest-tree;
It grinds to dust the harden'd brass,
Though stout and firm it be.

And yet this beast, that none can tame,
Its threat ne'er twice fulfils;
It dies in its self-kindled flame,
And dies e'en when it kills.
                    -Friederich von Schiller

Answer #122

159.

I live within a dwelling of stone,
There buried in slumber I dally;
Yet, armed with a weapon of iron alone,
The foe to encounter I sally.
At first I'm invisible, feeble, and mean,
And o'er me thy breath has dominion;
I'm easily drowned in a raindrop e'en,
Yet in victory waxes my pinion.
When my sister, all-powerful, gives me her hand,
To the terrible lord of the world I expand.
        -Friederich Schiller

Answer #154

160.

God made Adam out of the dust,
But thought it best to make me first.
So I was made before the man,
according to God's Holy plan.
My whole body God made complete,
without arms, or hands, or feet.
My ways and acts did God control,
but in my body He placed no soul.
A living being I became,
and Adam gave to me a name.
Then from his presence I withdrew,

for this man Adam I never knew.
All my Maker's laws I do obey,
and from these laws I never stray.
Thousands of me go in fear,
but seldom on the earth appear.
Later, for a purpose God did see,
He placed a living soul in me.
But that soul of mine God had to claim,
and from me took it back again.
And when this soul from me had fled,
I was the same as when first made;
without arms, legs, feet, or soul,
I travel on from pole to pole.
My labors are from day to night,
and to men I once furnished light.
Thousands of people both young and old,
did by my death bright lights behold.
No right or wrong can I conceive;
the Bible and it's teachings I can't believe.
The fear of death doesn't trouble me;
pure happiness I will never see.
And up in Heaven I can never go,
nor in the grave or hell below.
So get your Bible and read with care;
you'll find my name recorded there.

Answer #160

161.

In the ground my head is buried,
Yet with care I'm never harried.
In my early youth and fresh,
White and tender is my flesh,
Green my tail; of lowly plight,
The rich man's scorn, the boor's delight.
The peaseant on me sets good store,
The noble casts me from his door.
                    ~ Straparola

Answer #165

162.

Though wounded with iron
And smitten with war blade
I am first into battle
Wherever the foe.
No leech heals my scars,
No binding, my wounds,
But still I do battle
'Til riven in twain.

Answer #96

163.

My beak is bent downward, I burrow below;
I grub in the ground and go as he guides,
My master and I are foes of the forest.
Stoop-shouldered my warder walks at my back,
Fares through the field, urges and drives me,
Sows in my track as I sniff along.
Fetched from the wood, cunningly fitted,
Brought in a wagon, I have wondrous skill.
As I go my way on one side is green;
On the other side plain is my dark path.
Set through my back hangs a cunning spike; Another
fixed forward is fast to my head.
What I tear with my teeth falls to one side,
If he handles me right who is my ruler.

Answer #125

164.

I throw it white, it falls back yellow.

Answer #158

165.

Though I, alas! a prisoner be,
My trade is prisoners to set free.
No slave his lord's commands obeys
With such insinuating ways.
My genius piercing, sharp, and bright,
Wherein the men of wit delight.
The clergy keep me for their ease,
And turn and wind me as they please.
A new and wondrous art I show
Of raising spirits from below;
In scarlet some, and some in white;
They rise, walk round, yet never fright
In at each mouth the spirits pass,
Distinctly seen as through a glass.
O'er head and body make a rout,
And drive at last all secrets out;
And still, the more I show my art,
The more they open every heart.
A greater chemist none than I
Who, from materials hard and dry,
Have taught men to extract with skill
More precious juice than from a still.
Although I'm often out of case,
I'm not ashamed to show my face.
Though at the tables of the great
I near the sideboard take my seat;
Yet the plain 'squire, when dinner's done,
Is never pleased till I make one;
He kindly bids me near him stand,
And often takes me by the hand.
I twice a-day a-hunting go,

And never fail to seize my foe;
And when I have him by the poll,
I drag him upward from his hole;
Though some are of so stubborn kind,
I'm forced to leave a limb behind.
I hourly wait some fatal end;
For I can break, but scorn to bend.
                    -Jonathan Swift

Answer #163

166.

To cross the water, I'm the way,
For water I'm above:
I touch it not, and, truth to say,
I neither swim nor move.

Answer #156

167.

A low-bred squire,
Born in the mire,
That never knew who was his sire,

Being armed light,
After midnight,
He would needs go fight.

In corslet bad
The youth was clad,
And sarcenet sleeves in truth he had.

But at a word:
He had no sword,
Nor other weapon worth a word.

Nor was he strong
Nor large nor long,
But forth he came with hedeious song.

And Tartar leeke,
He me did seek
Lighting at first full on my cheek.

This thing of naught
At face still raught,
As Cesar once his soldier taught,

When they should fight
Against that knight,
Pompey defending countries right:

So in like case
This varlet base
Was ever poring at my face.

I could not rest
Within my nest,
The rascal did me so molest.

I had the Jack
Soon brought to wrack
Had he not ever retired back.

But he comes, he goes,
He fell, he rose,
He bit me by the very nose.

It made me swear
And God to tear,
I could not for my life forbear.

That such a knave
should be so brave,
Would make (I vow) a saint to rave.

But clod or stone,
Or stick or bone,
Or gun or crossbow had I none.

That, truth to show,
I did not know,
Which way I might him overthrow.

So that at last
I waxed aghast,
And, longing t' have the combat past,

I hid my head
Within a bed
And slept like one that had been dead.

Answer #167

168.

Inside me the adventurous find
Quests and treasures of every kind.
Trolls, goblins, orcs, and more,
Await within my closed walls for
All those that wish to visit me.
Your hands are the key
To secrets untold,
And your mind will unlock the door.

Answer #14

169.

Without a bridle,
Or a saddle,
Across a thing
I Ride a-straddle.
And those I ride
by help of me,
Though almost blind
Are made to see.

Answer #171

170.

I am standing,
He is lying down;
I am lying,
He is standing.

Answer #116

171.

I am the beginning of sorrow,
And the end of sickness.
You cannot express happiness without me;
Yet I am in the midsts of crosses.
I am always in risk,
Yet never in danger.
You may find me in the sun,
But I am never out of darkness.

Answer #166

172.

What has roots as nobody sees,
Is taller than the trees,
Up, up it goes,
And yet never grows?
                    -J.R.R. Tolkien

Answer #18

173.

Voiceless it cries,
Wingless flutters,
Toothless bites,
Mouthless mutters.
-J.R.R. Tolkien

Answer #97

174.

It cannot be seen, cannot be felt,
Cannot be heard, cannot be smelt.
It lies behind stars and under hills,
And empty holes it fills.
It comes first and follows after.
Ends life, kills laughter.
-J.R.R. Tolkien

Answer #31

175.

Alive without breath,
As cold as death;
Never thirsty, ever drinking,
All in mail never clinking.
-J.R.R. Tolkien

Answer #98

176.

An eye in a blue face
Saw an eye in a green face.
'That eye is like to this eye,'
Said the first eye,
'But in low place,
Not in high place.'
-J.R.R. Tolkien

Answer #9

177.

No-legs lay on one-leg
Two-legs sat near on three-legs,
Four-legs got some.
　　　　　-J.R.R. Tolkien

Answer #114

178.

This thing all things devours;
Birds, beasts, trees, flowers;
Gnaws iron, bites steel;
Grinds hard stones to meal;
Slays king, ruins town,
And beats high mountain down.
　　　　　-J.R.R. Tolkien

Answer #74

179.

What have I got in my pockets?

Answer #172

Answer Key

1. Spider's web.

2. A candle.

3. Spark.

4. Sieve or sponge.

5. Wind

6. Smoke.

7. Sun light.

8. Bed.

9. Sun on the daisies.

10. Candle.

11. The Letter 'H'.

12. Lice.

13. Pocket watch.

14. Book.

15. Stove, fire, and smoke.

16. Scandal.

17. Embers in the fire.

18. A mountain.

19. A button on a boy's shirt.

20. Shadow.

21. Sunshine.

22. Anger, greed, saints, cruel men.

23. Sun.

24. Glacier.

25. A ship's nail.

26. A cherry.

27. Silence.

28. Two - the three men are the same person.

29. Rainbow made by God.

30. The mist.

31. Darkness.

32. Water freezes to ice, ice thaws back to water.

33. Teeth and tongue.

34. Shoe.

35. Wedding ring.

36. A church with its steeple

37. An egg. The lines describe the shell, the papery stuff, the white, and the yolk.

38. Railroad.

39. Daffodils.

40. Frost.

41. A man with one eye saw the only two plums, he took one plum and left the other.

42. Anemone.

43. Sand.

44. Cow - eyes, horns, teats, and tail.

45. A hen egg.

46. The letter 'V'.

47. Man - He crawls in infancy, walks in maturity, hobbles with a cane in old age.

48. Counterfeit money.

49. Ship.

50. Adam.

51. Chimney.

52. Blue.

53. Obscurity.

54. Snail.

55. Stable.

56. Months of the year.

57. Bed.

58. Book-moth.

59. Fish in river.

60. An icicle.

61. River.

62. Needle and thread.

63. A horse drawn by a pen.

64. Quill pen.

65. The letter 'E'.

66. Rooster.

67. Stars.

68. Forehead, eyes, cheeks, nose, mouth and chin.

69. Shadow.

70. Telescope.

71. Glove.

72. Swan.

73. Your word.

74. Time.

75. River.

76. A kiss.

77. The corpse of the lion Samson killed was filled with honey from an infestation of honey bees.

78. A well.

79. In order, she gave a cherry blossom, an egg, a rolling thimble, and a sleeping baby.

80. Fire.

81. A cabbage.

82. Tomorrow.

83. Nothing.

84. Echo

85. Vowels.

86. Stopcock.

87. Coal.

88. Eye.

89. Slave's galley.

90. Nothing.

91. A broom.

92. Harp.

116. The foot.

117. Horn.

118. Walnut.

119. Fire.

120. The sun.

121. A star.

122. Lightning.

123. Which One.

124. Courtship.

125. Plow.

126. Few.

127. Drum.

128. Fireworks.

129. To write and to read.

130. Reflection.

131. Icicle.

132. Cipher.

133. Smoke.

134. Cuckoo.

135. Echo.

136. Coffin.

137. Wine.

138. Glove.

139. Heart.

93. Walnut.

94. DAVID (Roman numerals)

95. Your breath.

96. Shield.

97. Wind.

98. Fish.

99. Gold.

100. The gallows-maker - his frame outlives a thousand tenants.

101. Coal.

102. Honey-mead.

103. Cares.

104. Iceberg.

105. Pi (digits given by length of words).

106. Pig after roasting.

107. Flag.

108. Cannon.

109. Your reflection.

110. Anchor.

111. Bell.

112. Cuckoo.

113. An equal.

114. Fish on a table, man on the stool, cat gets bones.

115. A sieve.

140. Wagon wheel.

141. A rooster.

142. Pearl.

143. Thorn.

144. Watermelon.

145. Roasting meat on a spit.

146. Time.

147. Hen.

148. The ocean.

149. Candle.

150. Peanut.

151. A horse-drawn plow.

152. Gold.

153. Water.

154. Spark.

155. Eve.

156. Bridge.

157. A rubber ball.

158. An egg.

159. A one-eyed man selling garlic.

160. Whale.

161. Rooster.

162. A tennis ball.

163. A corkscrew.

164. The gallows.

165. The leek.

166. The letter 'S'.

167. A gnat.

168. The sea.

169. A bellows.

170. Snow melted by the sun.

171. Spectacles.

172. Now there's a poser.

Printed in Poland
by Amazon Fulfillment
Poland Sp. z o.o., Wrocław

65594006R00056